A Magic Carpet Ride

Primary Activities with Fairy Tales

Written by **Joan Vydra**

Illustrated by **Jean Thornley**

Table of Contents

Introduction

Fairy tales are the traditional literature of young children. Nearly every child has heard the wonderful stories that weave fantasy, magic, goodness, evil, and happy endings together to produce timeless tales. Fairy tales have endured for generations, continuing to open a world of fantasy and good versus evil while sparking children's imaginations. The appeal of fairy tales transcends the boundaries of countries, cultures, and time. They are stories for all children in all countries at all times.

Because of this inherent interest in and love for fairy tales, they are the perfect vehicle for building language skills and developing creative thinking. This guide offers students an opportunity to work their own magic—to create new ideas, to embellish, and to look at things from a new perspective. The exercises in this unit are designed to build language skills of primary students, but also to allow them to explore the world of fantasy by using their own imaginations. They will not only read fairy tales, but they will be thrust into the fairy tale world as they become fairy tale characters, find new solutions, analyze characteristics, clarify values, and make judgements.

An Integrated Language Experience

This curriculum guide on fairy tales uses an integrated approach to provide a variety of activities for whole-class instruction, small-group instruction, and individualized learning. When taught as an integrated unit, each activity compliments other activities and allows students to become skilled users of language and competent thinkers.

As we teach children to become critical readers, we find that they become more aware of authors' styles and the messages written into literature. They learn to apply what they have learned from one situation to another, to analyze what they have read, and to make judgements about the values portrayed in the literature.

As critical reading skills are sharpened, it is also important to develop creative reading skills. To do this, divergent thinking is rewarded and students are urged to synthesize, integrate, apply, and extend what they have read.

Creative reading leads to creative writing as students are asked to describe a character or enhance a new a character that they have read about, place themselves in a story situation, change an ending, or respond to an author. Writing, more than any other skill, demands the use of many levels of thinking. Also as students write, they become more critical of what they read. Suddenly they sense the power that an author has when they become authors themselves.

Also included in this process are students' oral language skills, which must be developed as the last link in the art of communication. Children speak before they read or write, yet this area is often neglected. If stimulating questions are asked, which children are asked to answer orally, they will develop oral language as well as creative thinking skills.

Teaching Fairy Tales

Fairy tales are a delightful form of literature that students read eagerly. These timeless stories also provide an excellent place to begin an in-depth analysis of story development, since fairy tales generally follow the same format of "happily ever after" and the virtues of truth and good almost always triumph over the forces of evil.

Depending on your classroom and media center resources, fairy tales can be read and enjoyed in a variety of ways. Some can be read aloud as a whole-class activity, some read in small groups, others read with partners or read individually. Still other fairy tales can be viewed on filmstrips, movies, or even listened to on records or cassettes.

In a learning environment that allows for maximum development of a child's thinking, learning, and creative abilities, it is important to provide activities that extend and enrich. This can be done with the puzzles, worksheets, and activities included in this book. The activities and worksheets are designed to build knowledge of individual fairy tales while comparing elements of several fairy tales, and analyzing common characteristics.

Objectives

Some educational objectives presented in this book are:

1. Children will demonstrate **comprehension** of fairy tales and **creative** thinking by combining their understanding with creative thinking to generate original but relevant ideas.

2. Students will enhance their **critical reading skills** through analysis of what they have read.

3. Students will develop their **creative reading skills** as they extend and respond to what they have read.

4. Students will build their **creative thinking** and **writing skills** as they communicate their original ideas about the stories in writing.

5. Students will use **logic** and **critical reasoning** to solve puzzles based on fairy tales.

Group Lessons

Lesson 1 - Introduction

Brainstorm with students a list of all the fairy tales they can remember. If a nursery rhyme is given, discuss the difference between a nursery rhyme and a fairy tale. When students cannot provide any additional titles, stop and discuss the characteristics of a fairy tale. At this time you may also wish to watch a movie or film-strip of a fairy tale and discuss the concept of good triumphing over evil.

Lesson 2 - Favorites

Using the list of fairy tales generated in lesson one, have students select their favorite fairy tale. Graph the results on a large chart. Make sure that students understand how the chart represents their choices.

Lesson 3 - Analyzing Fairy Tales

Select a fairy tale not listed during lesson one. Either read the story to the students or show a filmstrip or film of it. Discuss the forces of good and evil and the concept of make-believe. Discuss if the fairy tale could really happen, and if not, why.

Lesson 4 – Authors

Using books and anthologies, have students find the authors of several fairy tales and list them on the board. Discuss why so many stories are written by the same authors. Start an authors' bulletin board, concentrating on a few of the more well-known authors (the Grimm brothers, Hans Christian Anderson, Charles Perrault). Have students make book jackets to decorate the bulletin board. Add short biographical sketches of the authors and maps of their native countries.

Lesson 5 – Puppets

Using groups (perhaps reading groups), let students make paper bag puppets of fairy tale characters. Use the puppets to tell the fairy tale. Let students choose the fairy tale they want to use, but make sure that each student selects a different story.

Lesson 6 – Thumbelina

Read the story of Thumbelina to the whole class. Discuss what it would be like to be so small and live in the world as we know it. Have students work in small groups to list some of the things that Thumbelina could use, such as a walnut shell for a bathtub, pencils for a log house, etc.

Lesson 7 - Beginnings and Endings

Ask students to discover the usual opening to fairy tales ("Once upon a time...") and the usual ending ("They lived happily ever after"). Discuss why these phrases have become such a standard part of fairy tales and if other beginnings and endings would work as well. You will want students to understand that the beginning phrase is used to let people know that the fairy tale took place in the past, without having to be specific as to the time. The familiar ending is consistent with good triumphing over evil. Ask student to try and find a fairy tale that doesn't start or end in this familiar fashion.

Lesson 8 - Greed

After reading Beauty and the Beast, students will be ready for a discussion of greed. Beauty remained cheerful and brave, never complaining even after her father had lost his fortune and the family was forced to live in poverty. Her sisters, however, were very greedy and complained all the time. If Beauty had also been greedy, would the story have had a different ending? Students can brainstorm other characteristics of Beauty and her sisters, clarifying some of their values. Students can also find other fairy tale characters who are greedy and discuss the consequences of their greed.

Lesson 9 - Fairy Tale Cartoons

Start with a discussion of cartoons, and ask students if any of the fairy tales could be continuing episodes of cartoons. For instance, if Pinocchio was a cartoon character, what types of episodes could be written about his habit of lying? Divide students into small groups to write individual episodes following the elements of a good plot.

Lesson 10 - Combining Tales

In small groups, have students pick characters from two different fairy tales and combine the two into one fairy tale. The new fairy tales can then be shared with the rest of the class.

Lesson 11 - Revised for Movies

Read the original version of Snow White and the Seven Dwarfs and then compare it to the Walt Disney version. What changes were made? Why were those changes made? Make a chart of some of the differences, discussing why the changes might have been made. The concept that the children should realize as a result of the discussion is that the movie version was changed to make it more appealing and romantic for the audience. Movie-goers like seeing a dwarf with special characteristics, which is not the case with the original fairy tale. Discuss what changes would have to be made in other fairy tales to make them appealing to movie-goers.

Lesson 12 - Gifts

Let students make a gift for a fairy tale character, using their imagination and whatever materials are available in the classroom. The gift might be something that the fairy tale character could use to get out of a difficult situation or solve his/her problem.

Lesson 13 - Visualizing

Distribute copies of a fairy tale that is unfamiliar to students and has no illustrations. Ask students to depict what the characters and setting look like and create a title for the story. When complete, have them share their sketches with the rest of the class.

Lesson 14 - Characterization

Have students pretend that they are a fairy tale character. Then have students write or tell about their problems, feelings, dreams, hopes, etc. You may want to limit students' choices to certain characters who you feel would be easy to identify with or who exemplify certain values.

Lesson 15 - Coat of Arms

Have students design a coat of arms for Cinderella, Rapunzel, Thumbelina, Sleeping Beauty, or Beauty. All of these fairy tale characters married handsome princes and lived happily ever after. Students should use the following as a guide in their design and coloring:
    red - sacrifice and bravery
    purple - royalty
    white - faith
    yellow - honor
    blue - sincerity
    black - sorrow
    green - hope
    orange - strength
At the conclusion, let each student explain his/her coat of arms and what it represents. Display students' work on a bulletin board.

Lesson 16 - Fairy Tale Masquerade

Ask students to select a favorite fairy tale character and come to class dressed as this character. If several students have selected characters from the same story, put them together in one group. Then have students tell or act out their fairy tales either individually or as a group.

Lesson 17 - Comparing Countries

Read fairy tales from different countries—several from each country. Then compare how the stories are the same and different. What things are characteristic of stories from each country? What do these stories tell us about the country?

Lesson 18 - Characteristics

Ask students to be thinking about the special characteristics of fairy tales as they read. Then create a bulletin board that has some of these characteristics as headlines. Have students write the titles of stories that exemplify these characteristics under each headline. Possible headlines are:
    magic
    evil people
    things in threes
    good people rewarded
    prince and princess
    animals that talk
    witches
    magic spells
    things that could't happen in real life
    evil people are punished

Lesson 19 - Moral of the Story

Discuss with students that the moral of the story is the lesson or the message the story is trying to teach the reader. It usually tells how you should act if you want certain things to happen. Discuss what morals are demonstrated by various fairy tales the class has read. Or give students a moral and ask them which stories they have read teach this moral. Some possibilities for morals are:
    · Good things come to good people.
    · It doesn't pay to be evil.
    · By using your head, you can solve your problems.
    · Patience has its rewards.
    · Pretty is as pretty does.
    · Little friends may prove to be great friends.

Reading Record

Fill in the square by the title when you have read the fairy tale.

- ☐ Cinderella
- ☐ Jack and the Beanstalk
- ☐ Rapunzel
- ☐ Snow White
- ☐ The Frog Prince
- ☐ Little Red Riding Hood
- ☐ Goldilocks
- ☐ Three Billy Goats Gruff
- ☐ Musicians of Bremen
- ☐ Three Little Pigs
- ☐ Hansel and Gretel
- ☐ Ali Baba and the Forty Thieves
- ☐ Puss in Boots
- ☐ Rumpelstiltskin
- ☐ The Pied Piper of Hamelin
- ☐ The Ugly Duckling
- ☐ Wild Swans
- ☐ Seven in One Blow
- ☐ Three Dwarfs in the Woods
- ☐ Hans in Luck
- ☐ The Princess and the Pea

- ☐ The Shepherdess and the Chimney Sweep
- ☐ The Little Tin Soldier
- ☐ Thumbelina
- ☐ The Emperor's New Clothes
- ☐ The Fisherman and His Wife
- ☐ The Goose Girl
- ☐ The Golden Goose
- ☐ Sleeping Beauty
- ☐ Bluebeard
- ☐ Diamonds and Toads
- ☐ Aladdin
- ☐ Jack the Giant Killer
- ☐ Rip Van Winkle
- ☐ _____
- ☐ _____
- ☐ _____
- ☐ _____
- ☐ _____

Name _____

Fairy Tale Words

Here is a list of words that are often found in fairy tales. After each word, write down any other words that come to mind when you think of this word. There aren't any right or wrong answers, so let your imagination go and write what ever comes to mind.

1. witch _____

2. tale _____

3. forest _____

4. dwarf _____

5. treasure _____

6. cottage _____

7. enchanted _____

8. dungeon _____

9. elf _____

10. wicked _____

11. good _____

12. coach _____

13. evil _____

14. magical _____

Something Extra
Using the words above, create your own fantastic fairy tale sentences.

8

Grouping

Each line contains four words. Three of the words belong together because they have something in common. Write the word that doesn't belong and explain your choice.

1. Rapunzel, Cinderella, Snow White, Goldilocks
_____ doesn't belong because _____

2. princess, witch, king, prince,
_____ doesn't belong because _____

3. hen, harp, wand, money bags
_____ doesn't belong because _____

4. dragon, alligator, troll, unicorn,
_____ doesn't belong because _____

5. paper, wood, bricks, straw
_____ doesn't belong because _____

6. fairy, witch, magician, king
_____ doesn't belong because _____

7. Ugly Duckling, Ali Baba, the Three Bears, Puss in Boots
_____ doesn't belong because _____

Something Extra
Make up your own group of fairy tale words so that all but one of the words is related in some way. Give your problem to a friend to solve.

A Pair of Jacks

Read the two fairy tales, *Jack and the Beanstalk* and *Jack, the Giant Killer*. Are the two Jacks alike or are they different? Listed below are adjectives that could be used to describe one of the two Jacks or possibly both of them. Decide which Jack the adjective describes or if it might be used to describe both. Make a check in the correct box to show which Jack the word describes.

	Jack and the Beanstalk	Jack the Giant Killer	Both
1. brave			
2. greedy			
3. smart			
4. young			
5. witty			
6. poor			
7. good			
8. bold			

Something Extra
Explain your answers to a friend.

Name _____

Magic Prizes

Fairy tales tell about magic people, objects, spells, and even places. Pretend you can have one of these magic prizes. Which prize would you like? Give reasons for your choice.

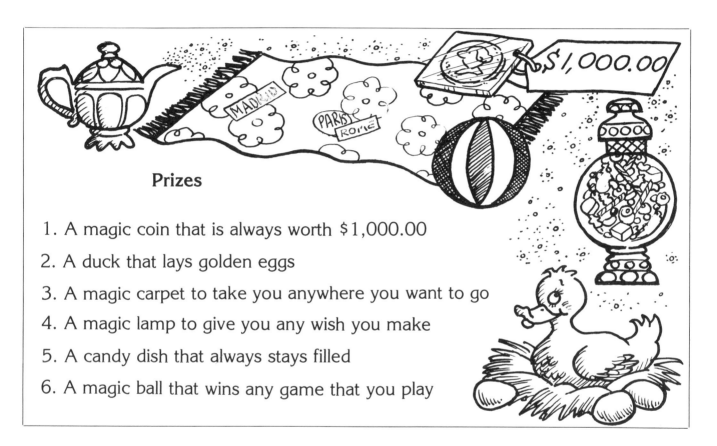

Prizes

1. A magic coin that is always worth $1,000.00
2. A duck that lays golden eggs
3. A magic carpet to take you anywhere you want to go
4. A magic lamp to give you any wish you make
5. A candy dish that always stays filled
6. A magic ball that wins any game that you play

What prize would you choose? _____

Why? _____

_____

What prize would be your least favorite? _____

Why? _____

_____

Something Extra
What other magic prizes can you think of? Make a list of three other prizes.

Name _____

Similarities and Differences

Each line contains two words. Think about the meanings of the words and how they might be the same. List some of the ways they are the same. Then think about how they are different. List some of the differences.

1. princess, king _____

_____

2. dream, wish _____

_____

3. dragon, frog _____

_____

4. monster, giant _____

_____

5. good, evil _____

_____

6. castle, cottage _____

_____

© Copyright 1986 Dandy Lion Publications—A Magic Carpet Ride

Name _____

Synonyms

In the Walt Disney movie of Snow White and the Seven Dwarfs, the dwarfs have names that describe what they are like or what they do. Here is a list of synonyms for each dwarf's name. Match each of the words in the word box that describe the dwarfs with the word that means the same or almost the same.

1. tired _____

2. physician _____

3. shy _____

4. sniffle _____

5. crabby _____

6. silly _____

7. joyful _____

Word Box

dopey   happy   doctor (doc)   bashful   grumpy   sneeze   sleepy

---

Something Extra

What if you could add an eighth dwarf? What would you name him?

My eighth dwarf would be named _____

Describe what he would be like. _____

_____

_____

On the back of this piece of paper, draw a picture of the eighth dwarf doing something he does very well.

Name _____

Dear Friend

Here are two lists of fairy tale characters. Choose one character from the first list and one from the second list. Then pretend you are one of the characters and write a letter to the other character.

List 1

Cinderella
Aladdin
Bluebeard
The Wicked Witch
Jack (and the Beanstalk)

List 2

Hansel
Sleeping Beauty
Snow White
Grumpy
Frog Prince

Dear _____

_____

_____

_____

_____

_____

_____

_____

_____

_____

Sincerely,

_____

What If

Choose one of these situations. Think about how the story would be different if this event had taken place. Write a new ending for the story showing what might have happened.

- What if Goldilocks had found the three bears at home?

- What if the fairy godmother had given Cinderella a new dress but no coach?

- What if there were eight brothers instead of seven in "Wild Swans"?

- What if Ali Baba's brother had remembered the magic word and escaped?

- What if the Pied Piper had played a piano?

- What if the prince had been changed into a cat instead of a frog?

- What if Red Riding Hood's father had not heard her screams?

- What if Cinderella's two sisters were beautiful?

A Magical Event

This bottle is full of magic. Think of how you could use the magic in the bottle to solve a problem in a fairy tale. Draw a picture and describe how you would use the magic.

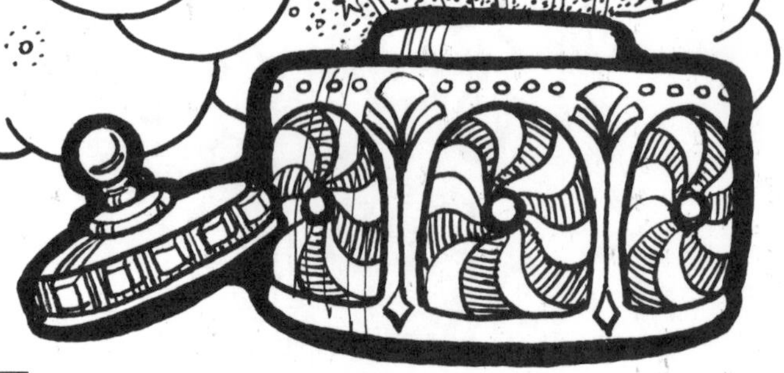

_____

_____

_____

_____

_____

_____

_____

_____

_____

Name _____

Once Upon a Time

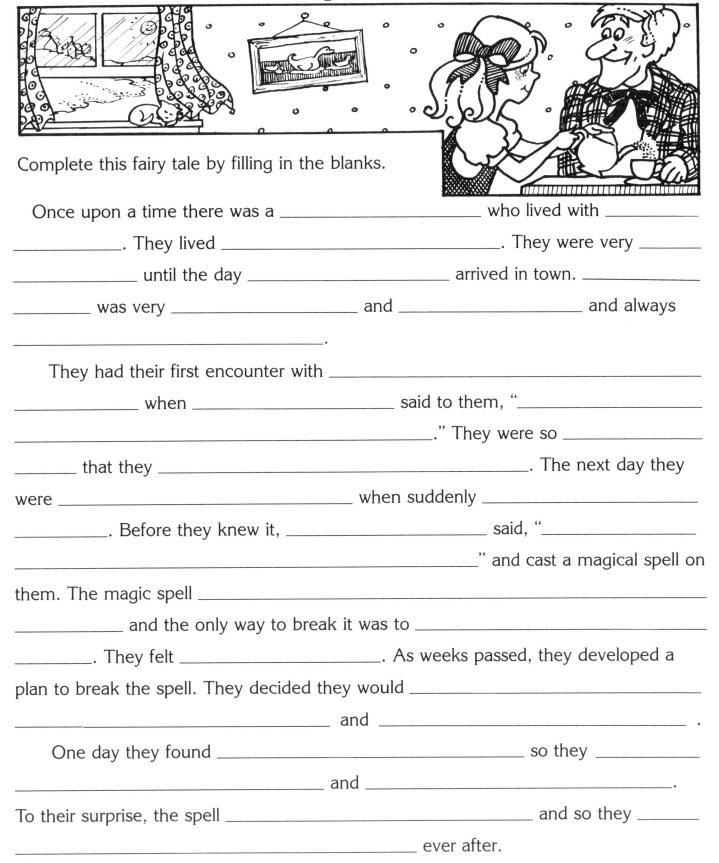

Complete this fairy tale by filling in the blanks.

Once upon a time there was a _____ who lived with _____

_____. They lived _____. They were very _____

_____ until the day _____ arrived in town. _____

_____ was very _____ and _____ and always

_____.

They had their first encounter with _____

_____ when _____ said to them, "_____

_____." They were so _____

_____ that they _____. The next day they

were _____ when suddenly _____

_____. Before they knew it, _____ said, "_____

_____" and cast a magical spell on

them. The magic spell _____

_____ and the only way to break it was to _____

_____. They felt _____. As weeks passed, they developed a

plan to break the spell. They decided they would _____

_____ and _____ .

One day they found _____ so they _____

_____ and _____.

To their surprise, the spell _____ and so they _____

_____ ever after.

Name _____

Fairy Godmother

What fairy tales have you read that have good fairies or fairy godmothers in them?

_____

_____

_____

_____

If you had a good fairy godmother who said she would grant you three wishes, what would they be? Why would you choose each wish?

Wish 1 · A wish for yourself

_____

_____

I would want this because _____

_____

Wish 2 · A wish for your family

_____

_____

I would want this because _____

_____

Wish 3 · A wish for all people of the world

_____

_____

I would want this because _____

_____

What Is the Question?

Think about the fairy tales you have read. Here are some answers that could be answers to questions about different fairy tales. Write a question that would go with each answer.

1. The answer is **the wicked witch**. What is the question?

_____

2. The answer is **long, golden hair**. What is the question?

_____

3. The answer is **two ugly sisters**. What is the question?

_____

4. The answer is **lost in the woods**. What is the question?

_____

5. The answer is **the giant**. What is the question?

_____

6. The answer is **magic spell**. What is the question?

_____

7. The answer is **animals that talk**. What is the question?

_____

Something Extra
Write an answer for a fairy tale question. Give your answer to a friend. Ask your friend to write the question that goes with the answer.

Name _____

Telegramming

Little Red Riding Hood wants to send a message to her grandmother, but she only has enough money to pay for 25 words. Read the message and then decide what words you can take out without changing the message. Names are considered words.

To Grandmother,
While walking to your house this morning, I met a wolf. Not knowing what a wicked beast he was, I told him where I was going. He arrived at your house before I did, put on your cap and crept under your bedclothes. I did not recognize him and began talking with him. My father saved me and chased the wolf away. You may expect me to visit you tomorrow.

Love,
Little Red Riding Hood

New Message
_____
_____
_____
_____ total number of words _____

Something Extra
Write a telegram from one fairy tale character to another that could change the happenings in the story.

Real or Fantasy?

Some of the things that happen in fairy tales are real and some are fantasy. Here is a list of events. Some are real—they could happen in real life. Some are fantasy—they could not happen in real life. Decide if each event is real or fantasy and mark the correct box. Then match the event with the correct fairy tale.

Real Fantasy

1. [R] [F]   Children get lost in the woods.

2. [R] [F]   Cats talk and wear boots.

3. [R] [F]   Beanstalks grow to the sky.

4. [R] [F]   Sisters are jealous of each other.

5. [R] [F]   People sleep for 100 years.

6. [R] [F]   Children are fooled by somebody who asks directions in a nice way.

7. [R] [F]   People make fun of others because they don't look like everyone else.

8. [R] [F]   People can spin straw into gold.

9. [R] [F]   People fall in love and get married.

_____ Rumpelstiltskin

_____ Cinderella

_____ Ugly Duckling

_____ Snow White

_____ Jack and the Beanstalk

_____ Sleeping Beauty

_____ Little Red Riding Hood

_____ Puss in Boots

_____ Hansel and Gretel

Fairy Tale Crossword Puzzle

Clues Across

2. Let down her hair.
4. Told too many lies.
7. There were seven of them.
9. Had a fairy godmother.
10. Jack traded this for the magic beans.
11. She tried to cook Hansel.
14. She slept for 100 years.
15. She entered the home of the bears.

Clues Down

1. Goldilocks was going to visit her.
3. He never thought anyone would guess his name.
5. Beauty learned to love him.
6. He led the children of Hamelin.
8. She was the fairest of them all.
12. What the queen put in the apple she gave to Snow White.
13. Cinderella fell in love with him.

Name _____

Good and Evil

Fairy tales usually have both good and evil.
Choose five fairy tales. For each story, list at
least one force of good and one of evil.

Story	Good	Evil
1.		
2.		
3.		
4.		
5.		

Does good always win over evil in fairy tales? _____

Why? _____

Something Extra
Finish these sentences by writing original ways to describe good and evil.

It was as good as _____

It was as evil as _____

Name _____

Favorite Fairy Tales

Fill in the title of your favorite fairy tale for each of the following things:

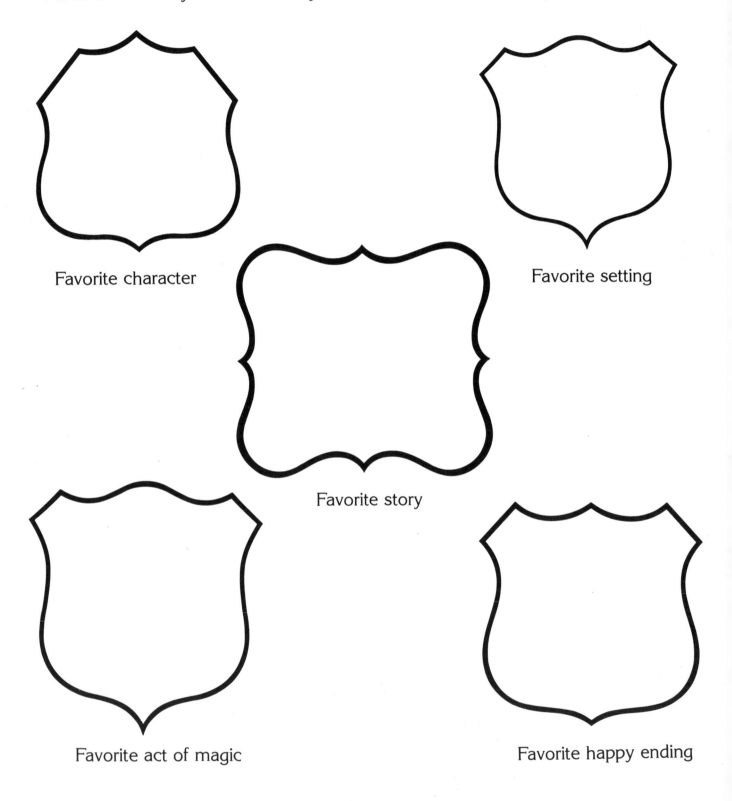

Favorite character

Favorite setting

Favorite story

Favorite act of magic

Favorite happy ending

Decorate each award to make it look different than the others.

Name _____

Comparing Stories

Choose a fairy tale and read two or three different versions of the same story. Then answer these questions.

What is the name of the fairy tale? _____

Author's name _____

How are the stories alike?

1. _____

2. _____

3. _____

How are the stories different?

1. _____

2. _____

3. _____

Which story did you like best? Why? _____

_____

_____

Something Extra
What would you change if you were writing your own version of this story?

Name _____

Eye Witness Report

Cinderella's fairy godmother used her magic to change a pumpkin into a beautiful coach. Imagine that you were there to see the change. Write an eye witness report describing exactly what happened. You might want to include comments or facts from other people who watched (by-standers).

Continue your report on another piece of paper.

Name _____

The Pied Piper of Hamelin

Read the story of the Pied Piper of Hamelin. Then imagine what happens to the children after the hill closes. Write a letter to the parents telling them what has happened to the children. Also tell how the children feel about this happening and what (if anything) they want their parents to do about it.

Dear Parents of Hamelin,

   I just wanted to tell you _____

_____

_____

_____

_____

_____

_____

_____

_____

                   Sincerely,

                   _____
                     (your name)

Name _____

Magic Names

Rumpelstiltskin's secret was his unusual name. You don't know what Rumpelstiltskin thought about his name, but what can you say about your own name? Write your name vertically down the middle of the paper. Then think of words that might describe you that begin with the letters in your name. Write the words next to each letter in your name.

For example, Rumpelstiltskin might write his name like this:

Remarkable

Unique

Mysterious

Pudgy

Extraordinary

Likable

Secretive

Talented

Impish

Lonesome

Tough

Superhuman

Keen

Intelligent

Nimble

Write your name and the words that describe you in this space.

Something Extra

Use your name or the name of a fairy tale character to write a name poem. Write the name as you did for this activity, but use several words or a phrase instead of a single word for each line.

Name _____

Magical Magic

What are some examples of magic
you have found in the fairy tales you
have read?

_____

_____

_____

_____

_____

_____

_____

Complete these sentences about magic.

1. Magic looks like _____

2. Magic sounds like _____

3. Magic smells like _____

4. Magic feels like _____

5. I am magic, I can _____

   _____

6. Magic can _____

   and _____

   and _____

7. Magic happens in everyday life when _____

   _____

A Fairy Tale Mystery

Here are some happenings from a fairy tale story. Put a number in the blank before each statement to show what happened first (1), what happened second (2), and what happened last (10).

_____ While walking through the forest, he came across a witch who was looking for her lost glasses. The witch said that she could not have stolen the colors because she could not see without her glasses.

_____ The goblin also said that while he was awake, he saw a lady walking through the woods with a basket in her hand.

_____ At the end of the rainbow, he laid the basket of magic mushrooms. They turned into a pot of gold and have been there ever since.

_____ The wicked fairy said that she had been in the woods all morning picking magic mushrooms. She could prove that she was doing this because she had a basket of mushrooms.

_____ Once upon a time a prince set out to find out who had stolen the colors from the rainbow.

_____ He asked her to prove that she had been looking for her glasses. She said to ask the goblin. She had tripped over him while stumbling through the woods.

_____ The prince followed the goblin's advice and traveled down the crooked path to the castle. There he found the wicked fairy.

_____ He went looking for the goblin and found him asleep under a mushroom. He said that he had been asleep all morning. He woke up only briefly when someone tripped on him.

_____ He grabbed the basket and ran through the woods. As he ran, he threw handfuls of color into the sky. Soon all the color was returned to the rainbow.

_____ The prince believed her until he saw a ray of color shining through the mushrooms.

Name _____

You Be the Judge

Choose one of these situations. Then pretend that you are the judge and decide whether the person or animal should be found guilty of the crime they are accused of committing.

Character	Crime
1. Goldilocks	breaking and entering
2. Pied Piper	kidnapping
3. Three Billy Goats	assault
4. Jack and the Beanstalk	robbery
5. Cinderella	impersonating a princess
6. Ali Baba	robbery

I hereby find _____ (guilty, not guilty), because _____

_____

_____

_____

_____

_____

_____

Something Extra
With your friends act out a trial of one of these fairy tale crimes. After you have presented evidence for and against the character, ask your class to decide whether the character is guilty or not guilty

Problem Solving

How good are you at solving problems? Choose one of these situations. Underline the problem you want to solve. Then make a long list of things you could do to solve the problem.

Problems

1. Two children are lost in the woods with nothing to eat.
2. Three pigs are locked inside a house with a hungry wolf outside.
3. Three goats want to get to a good pasture on the other side of the bridge, but a mean troll lives under the bridge.
4. A young girl is locked in a tall tower. The tower has only one window at the top and no doors.

To solve this problem I could...

_____

_____

_____

_____

_____

_____

_____

_____

_____

_____

_____

_____

_____

_____

Put a * by the solution that you think is the best.

Name _____

The Story Line

Stories usually include the same basic parts. The beginning or **introduction** of the story introduces the *setting*, the *time*, and the *characters*. The *setting* tells where and when the story takes place. The *time* tells when the story happened. The *characters* are the people who are in the story. Every story also includes a **story line** that includes the *problem*, the *climax*, and the *ending*. The *problem* begins the action of the story. It describes the problem that the character must solve or the obstacle he/she must overcome. The *climax* is the most exciting part of the story. This is where the problem is the biggest but before the character finds the solution to the problem. The *ending* solves the problem and closes the story.

introduction	**story line** (or **plot**)	climax
time characters setting	problem	ending

Choose a fairy tale and briefly describe the four parts of the story.

Story title _____

Time _____

Setting _____

_____

Characters _____

_____

Problem _____

_____

_____

Climax _____

_____

_____

Ending _____

_____

Create-a-Fairy Tale

Use the information about the parts of a story to create your own fairy tale. Before writing your story, use this outline to help you plan all the important parts of your fairy tale.

Characters - Introduce your good character and the other people or animals in your story who like this character. Also introduce your bad character and explain what makes this person evil.

Names   What character is like

_____

_____

_____

_____

_____

Setting and **Time** - Tell when and where your story takes place.

_____

_____

Problem - Is there something making your character sad, mad, or frightened? How does the bad character cause this problem, make it worse, or challenge your good character?

_____

_____

Climax - Place your character in a very scary or dangerous position. Plan how you will save the character from this dangerous spot.

_____

_____

Ending - Tell how the problem is solved and how the character is happier, smarter, or safer. Tell what happened to the bad character. Let the reader know that everything is all right.

_____

_____

Goldilocks Logic

Goldilocks, the 3 bears, and the wolf went on a picnic together in the forest. Goldilocks sat next to Mama Bear. Baby Bear sat next to the Wolf. Papa Bear sat in the third seat from Mama Bear. Goldilocks sat in the third seat from Baby Bear. Who sat where?

Cut out the pictures of the characters. Move them around into the correct positions. When you are sure you have the correct answer, glue the characters onto a piece of paper in the right positions.

Princely Logic

Four fairy tale princes rode off into the woods to capture dragons. One captured 8 dragons, one captured 6 dragons, one captured 4 dragons, and one captured 2 dragons. Use these clues to help you figure out how many dragons each prince captured.

1. Prince Jack captured more than Prince Ryan and Prince George.
2. Prince Jack captured less than Prince Jeff.
3. Prince Ryan captured less than Prince George.

How many dragons did each prince capture?

Prince Ryan _____

Prince Jeff _____

Prince George _____

Prince Jack _____

Dwarf Logic

Four dwarfs are bringing nature items from their woodland home to decorate the table for their favorite princess. The items they are bringing are daisies, nuts, colored leaves, and berries. Use the clues to help you figure out what each dwarf brought.

1. The first dwarf and the second dwarf are bringing things that are good to eat.
2. The third dwarf is allergic to flowers.
3. The second dwarf is allergic to berries.

	daisies	nuts	leaves	berries
first dwarf				
second dwarf				
third dwarf				
fourth dwarf				

Little Red Riding Hood

When the wolf was gone, Little Red Riding Hood, Grandma, and the woodcutter celebrated with dessert. One person had one helping, one had two helpings, and one had three helpings. One had cherry pie, one had chocolate cake, and one had rice pudding. Use the clues to help you figure out what each person ate.

1. The double helping was cherry pie.
2. Little Red Riding Hood loves rice pudding.
3. The woodcutter had more helpings than one of the females.
4. Grandma doesn't eat cherry pie or more than one helping.

	one	two	three	cherry pie	chocolate cake	rice pudding
woodcutter						
Grandma						
Red Riding Hood						
cherry pie						
chocolate cake						
rice pudding						

1 Magical Mapping

Choose one of these fairy tales and make a map of what you think the story setting would look like. Label where all the important happenings in the story take place.

Snow White

Pinocchio

Little Red Riding Hood

Hans in Luck

Thumbelina

The Ugly Duckling

2 Advertising

Create an advertisement for the Three Little Pigs Construction Company. Be sure to mention what they have learned from experience and describe the quality home they can build. Keep in mind what their forest customers would need in a home.

3 Animals

How are animals portrayed in fairy tales? Which animals usually stand for good? Which ones usually stand for evil?

Write a letter to the editor defending the wolf (or some other animal that is shown as evil in fairy tales). List all of its good qualities and describe the helpful services it could perform for people.

4 Wanted Poster

Make a wanted poster for one of the evil characters in a fairy tale. On this poster, draw a picture of this person and describe what crime this person has committed. Then describe what this person could do to make up for the crime and be forgiven.

5   Help Wanted

Write several help-wanted advertisements for jobs you might find in fairy tales. Include a description of the job and what qualifications the person must have. You might consider jobs like these:

- Dragon Slayer
- Magic Spell Breaker
- Gold Spinner
- Problem Solver
- Giant Tamer
- Witch Catcher

6   Groups of Three

How many things in fairy tales come in groups of threes—three characters, three wishes, three magical things, three houses? Make a poster, a book, or a mobile that shows as many groups of three as you can find.

7   A Word of Advice

What advice might some of the fairy tale characters have for children your age? Design a poster using fairy tale characters to share important advice about how to behave or what to do or not do.

8   Character Awards

Think about all the characters you have read about in fairy tales. Then decide who you would give these awards to.

- Most Evil and Wicked
- Most Daring and Brave
- Most Greedy
- Most Clever
- Most Forgiving
- Most Honest

What other award would you like to give to a fairy tale character?

9 Ingredients

What are all the things that make a good fairy tale? Make a list of the ingredients of a good fairy tale. Include instructions for how to combine these ingredients.

10 Another Point of View

In most fairy tales, we only know the story from the good character's point of view. Choose a fairy tale and imagine how the evil character must have felt. Rewrite the story from the evil character's point of view. Tell what this character was thinking. Make the audience see the other side of the story.

11 A New Ending

Read a fairy tale that you have never read before. Using colored pencils or crayons, draw five pictures that show the main events in the story. Write a sentence about each picture.

12 Creative Combinations

Combine the elements (characters, setting, problem) of one fairy tale with the elements of another fairy tale to make a new story. Tell or write your new story.

13 Create-a-Character

Imagine a new fairy tale character. Draw a picture of the new character. Describe what this person or animal is like. Tell whether you would want this character for a friend. Why?

14 Story Setting

Choose a favorite fairy tale. Make a shoe box diorama that shows the setting of the story. On a card write a paragraph that tells about the setting using descriptive words. Tape the card to the outside of the box.

15 A New Product

Think of a new, imaginary product that could help a fairy tale character solve his/her problem. Write or act out a scene that shows a salesperson selling this product to the character (describing all of the wonderful things it will do and how it will work) and what happens when the character uses the product.

16 Fairy Tale Game

Make a game for your friends to play that includes fairy tale characters, fairy tale facts and/or things you find in fairy tales (good, evil, magic, castles...).

Answers

Grouping

1. Goldilocks because she is a young girl and did not marry a prince.
2. Witch because the others are all royalty.
3. Wand because all the others are treasures from Jack and the Beanstalk.
4. Unicorn because all the others have negative connotations. Or troll because the others are animals.
5. Paper because the others are materials the pigs used to build their houses.
6. King because the others can make magic.
7. Ali Baba because the others are animals.

A Pair of Jacks

All choices are possible as long as students can defend their answers.

Similarities and Differences

Answers will vary but some possible answers are:
1. They are both members of royalty, they are both related to the queen, and they are usually the good people in fairy tales.
   One is young and one is older, one is a girl and one is a man, one is little and one is big, one is a ruler and one is not.
2. They both deal with things that might happen.
   A wish is something you consciously think about, a dream is something that can enter your thoughts when you are asleep.
3. Both are animals, both are in fairy tales, both can change forms.
   One is real and one is make believe, one breathes fire and one does not, one is large and one is small.
4. Both are imaginary characters, both can be very large, both are usually scary, both usually are the bad character in fairy tales.
   One is usually a person and one is usually an imaginary character that is neither a real animal or person.
5. Both describe people's actions, both can be found in fairy tales.
   One is something that most people like and one is something that people don't like, one is associated with the hero and one with the villain in a story.

6. Both are places to live.
   One is large and one is small, one is where royalty lives and one is where common people live.

Synonyms

1. tired - sleepy
2. physician - doctor
3. shy - bashful
4. sniffles - sneeze
5. crabby - grumpy
6. silly - dopey
7. joyful - happy

What Is the Question?

Answers may vary but possible answers are:
1. Who changed the prince into a frog?
2. What was special about Rapunzel?
3. Who lived with Cinderella?
4. Where were Hansel and Gretel after the birds ate their bread crumbs?
5. Who lived at the top of Jack's beanstalk?
6. What made Sleeping Beauty fall asleep?
7. What do the stories Puss in Boots and The Frog Prince have in common?

Telegramming

One possibility is:
To: Grandmother
Met wolf going to your house. Wolf disguised himself as you. Father chased him away. See you tomorrow.
Little Red Riding Hood

Real or Fantasy?

1. real · Hansel and Gretel
2. fantasy · Puss in Boots
3. fantasy · Jack and the Beanstalk
4. real · Cinderella
5. fantasy · Sleeping Beauty
6. real · Little Red Riding Hood
7. real · Ugly Duckling
8. fantasy · Rumpelstiltskin
9. real · Snow White

Fairy Tale Crossword Puzzle

Across
  2. Rapunzel
  4. Pinocchio
  7. dwarfs
  9. Cinderella
10. cow
11. witch
14. Sleeping Beauty
15. Goldilocks

Down
  1. Grandma
  3. Rumpelstiltskin
  5. Beast
  6. Pied Piper
  8. Snow White
12. poison
13. prince

A Fairy Tale Mystery

2 5 10 7 1 3 6 4 9 8

Goldilocks Logic

Goldilocks, Mama Bear, the wolf, Baby Bear, and Papa Bear

Princely Logic

Prince Ryan · 2
Prince Jeff · 8
Prince George · 4
Prince Jack · 6

Dwarf Logic

first dwarf · berries
second dwarf · colored leaves
third dwarf · nuts
fourth dwarf · daisies

Little Red Riding Hood

Little Red Riding Hood · 3, rice pudding
Woodcutter · 2, cherry pie
Grandma · 1 chocolate cake